by

Two R

by Liza Charlesworth

ISBN: 978-1-338-78270-7
Illustrated by Michael Robertson

Published by Scholastic Inc., 557 Broadway, New York, NY 10012

10 9 8 7 6 5 4 3 2 1 68 21 22 23 24 25 26 27/0

Printed in Jiaxing, China. First printing, June 2021.

One robot is **by** the truck.
One robot is **by** the duck.

One robot is **by** the ball.
One robot is **by** the wall.

One robot is **by** the sheep.
One robot is **by** the jeep.

One robot is **by** the flower.
One robot is **by** the tower.

One robot is **by** the dog.
One robot is **by** the frog.

One robot is **by** the rocks.
One robot is **by** the box.

Two robots are **by** the fox!